ExamREVIEW.NET

Please be aware that our practice questions are NOT "realistic questions" or "past exam questions". We do NOT provide questions for cheating purpose!

Intellectual Properties, Trademarks and Copyrights

ExamREVIEW(TM) and ExamFOCUS(TM) are our own trademarks for publishing and marketing self-developed examprep books worldwide. The EXAMREVIEW.NET web site has been created on the Internet since January 2001. The EXAMFOCUS.NET division has its web presence established since 2009.

newer version, all you need to do is to go and download. **Please check our web site's Free Updates section regularly:** *http://www.examreview.net/free_updates.htm*

The Book

In Hawaii, obtaining a Low Voltage Systems (LVS) contractor license is mandatory for anyone who wants to install, maintain, alter or repair any low voltage systems in the state of Hawaii. The DCCA requires four years of experience, passing an exam, and being at least 18 years old.

This book covers the trade exam. 220+ questions are included.

This product focuses on the technical aspect of low voltage works in general. It does not specifically cover fire alarm, satellite or other specific disciplines. **You should therefore use this product together with other study resources for the best possible exam prep coverage.**

Table of Contents

Question 1:

Alternating Current AC always flows one way then the other.

Possible Choices:

True

False

Answer:

True. Alternating Current AC always flows one way then the other – in other words, it travels continually with reversing directions. It is also continually changing between positive (+) and negative (−).

Question 2:

The frequency of AC is measured in:

Possible Choices:

Hz

MHz

KHz

Sz

Answer:

The rate of changing the direction is being referred to as the frequency of AC, which is measured in hertz Hz.

Question 3:

_____ refers to a voltage which can convey information.

Possible Choices:

Electrical signal

Electrical frequency

Electrical wave

Electrical pressure

Amplitude

Ampacity

Answer:

An electrical signal refers to a voltage which can convey information.

Question 4:

What refers to the maximum voltage that can be reached by a signal?

Possible Choices:

Electrical signal

Electrical frequency

Electrical wave

Electrical pressure

Amplitude

Ampacity

Answer:

Amplitude refers to the maximum voltage that can be reached by a signal, and is measured in volts.

Question 5:

Electricity may flow only when:

Possible Choices:

there is a complete circuit

there is no complete circuit

there is a frequency

there is a pressure

Answer:

Electricity describes the flow of charge around a circuit that carries power and energy. Electricity may flow only when there is a complete circuit – there has to be a way for return trip to be made.

Question 6:

_____ is the return path for electrical power to flow back to the service panel.

Possible Choices:

Ground

Electrode

Neutral

Live

Answer:

Neutral is the return path for electrical power to flow back to the service panel. Inside of the panel you will find the neutral wires bonded to the ground wires and also to a grounding conductor which connects that assembly to earth.

Question 7:

The live wire is always ungrounded.

Possible Choices:

True

False

Answer:

True. Live wires are "hot" wires that carry the electrical power. The live wire is an ungrounded conductor. The neutral wire is a grounded conductor.

Question 8:

A ground electrode conductor originates at the neutral or equipment ground bus of the service panel.

Possible Choices:

True

False

Answer:

A ground electrode conductor originates at the neutral or equipment ground bus of the service panel.

Question 9:

A ground electrode should not be made in contact with the earth.

Possible Choices:

True

False

Answer:

False. A ground electrode is in contact with the earth, which can be a building metal frame or an underground metallic pipe.

Question 10:

Compare Watts with Voltage.

Possible Choices:

Watts are the measure of power, while voltage is the measure of potential energy.

Voltage is the measure of power, while watts are the measure of potential energy.

Both are the measure of potential power.

Answer:

Watts are the measure of power, while voltage is the measure of potential energy. Amps measure the amount of electricity that pass a point in a given period of time.

Question 11:

You should size conductors no less than _____ of the continuous loads plus _____ of the non-continuous loads.

Possible Choices:

125% / 100%

125% / 150%

125% / 175%

100% / 100%

100% / 125%

Answer:

You should size conductors no less than 125% of the continuous loads plus 100% of the non-continuous loads.

Question 12:

Conductor sizes are often expressed in:

Possible Choices:

AWG

Hz

MHz

RWG

Answer:

Conductor sizes are often expressed in American Wire Gage (AWG). The American Wire Gauge system provides a standardized method for specifying wire sizes, allowing engineers, electricians, and manufacturers to select the appropriate wires for their specific applications based on current capacity, voltage rating, and other electrical requirements.

Question 13:

What refers to the allowable current-carrying capacity of a conductor?

Possible Choices:

Electrical signal

Electrical frequency

Electrical wave

Electrical pressure

Amplitude

Ampacity

Answer:

Ampacity is the allowable current-carrying capacity of a conductor. It is measured in amps. Ampacity refers to the maximum amount of electric current that a conductor, such as a wire or cable, can carry continuously without exceeding its temperature rating or causing damage. It is an essential consideration in electrical engineering and design to ensure safe and reliable operation of electrical systems.

Question 14:

The insulation type determines the areas the wires can and cannot be used.

Possible Choices:

True

False

Answer:

It is the insulation type that determines the areas the wires can and cannot be used. LV circuits often require specific types of insulation materials and wiring methods to provide adequate electrical insulation and mechanical protection. Proper insulation helps prevent electrical faults and short circuits that could compromise safety.

Question 15:

RHH wires use rubber insulation that is high heat resistant and is good in:

Possible Choices:

dry locations.

wet locations.

wet and dry locations.

Answer:

RHH wires use rubber insulation that is high heat resistant but is good only in dry locations.

Question 16:

RHW-2 wires use rubber insulation but are suitable for wet locations.

Possible Choices:

True

False

Answer:

True. RHW-2 wires also use rubber insulation but are suitable for wet locations.

Question 17:

_____cables can be used inside wall, ceiling or under the floor.

Possible Choices:

NM

RMM

RMM-2

TM

SM

UF

Answer:

NM cables can be used inside wall, ceiling or under the floor.

Question 18:

_____ cables are most appropriate for damp areas.

Possible Choices:

NM

RMM

RMM-2

TM

SM

UF

Answer:

UF/NMWU cables are appropriate for damp areas.

Question 19:

THWN means (choose all that apply):

Possible Choices:

flame retardant

heat resistant

moisture resistant

gasoline resistant

oil resistant

Answer:

THWN means flame retardant, heat resistant, moisture resistant, gasoline resistant, and oil resistant. THW means heat resistant, flame retardant, and moisture resistant only.

Question 20:

An insulated grounded conductor which is ___ AWG or below should be identified by a continuous white or gray outer finish

Possible Choices:

12

10

8

6

4

Answer:

An insulated grounded conductor which is 6 AWG or below should be identified by a continuous white or gray outer finish or by three continuous white stripes on other than green insulation along its entire length.

Question 21:

_____ is the amount of voltage measured between any two line conductors of a balanced three-phase system.

Possible Choices:

Line voltage

Point voltage

Spot voltage

Surface voltage

Phase voltage

Answer:

Line voltage is the amount of voltage measured between any two line conductors of a balanced three-phase system.

Question 22:

_____ describes the voltage measured across any one component of a balanced three-phase system.

Possible Choices:

Line voltage

Point voltage

Spot voltage

Surface voltage

Phase voltage

Answer:

Phase voltage describes the voltage measured across any one component of a balanced three-phase system.

Question 23:

A _____ is unintentional.

Possible Choices:

Ground Fault

Ground bond

Earth bond

Answer:

A Ground Fault describes an unintentional, electrically conducting connection between an ungrounded conductor of a circuit and a normally non-current-carrying conductor or anything metallic, or earth.

Question 24:

An Effective Ground-Fault Current Path is:

Possible Choices:

mostly intentional.

mostly unintentional.

Answer:

An Effective Ground-Fault Current Path is a path intentionally constructed to facilitate the operation of the overcurrent protective devices currently in place.

Question 25:

GFCI is never sensitive to small "leaks" of current.

Possible Choices:

True

False

Answer:

False. GFCI = ground-fault circuit interrupter. It is typically very sensitive to small "leaks" of current. Some said that GFCI is primarily for human protection against deadly shock.

Question 26:

Grounding and bonding mean exactly the same thing.

Possible Choices:

True

False

Answer:

You need to know that grounding and bonding do not mean exactly the same thing. Bonding is a means of allowing electrical continuity between metallic objects.

Question 27:

A typical work space (for a working voltage under 600V) should have a minimum headroom of _____ m.

Possible Choices:

1

1.5

2

2.5

3

5

Answer:

A typical work space (for a working voltage under 600V) should have a minimum headroom of 2.0 m and should be clear and extend from the grade, floor, or platform to the required height.

Question 28:

Typically there are ____ hot wires running from the utility company into the service panel.

Possible Choices:

2

3

4

5

6

Answer:

There are two hot wires and one neutral wire running from the utility company into the service panel. Older systems use only one hot wire which may not be scalable service-wise.

Question 29:

A service disconnect needs to have a rating which is:

Possible Choices:

no less than that of the calculated load for the type of installation.

no more than that of the calculated load for the type of installation.

no less than that of 120% of the calculated load for the type of installation.

no less than that of 130% of the calculated load for the type of installation.

no less than that of 150% of the calculated load for the type of installation.

Answer:

A service disconnect needs to have a rating which is no less than that of the calculated load or for the type of installation.

Question 30:

Fast-blow fuses tend to open real quick when the rated current is reached.

Possible Choices:

True

False

Answer:

Fast-blow fuses tend to open real quick when the rated current is reached. Slow-blow fuses may survive a transient overcurrent condition but will still get opened when the overcurrent condition is sustained.

Question 31:

System grounding is required when you have a supply transformer of a 50V or lower system:

Possible Choices:

which itself is supplied from a source over 150V to ground.

which itself is supplied from a source over 300V to ground.

which itself is supplied from a source over 600V to ground.

which itself is supplied from a source over 1000V to ground.

Answer:

System grounding is required when you have a supply transformer of a 50V or lower system which itself is supplied from a source over 150V to ground.

Question 32:

On a Class 1 Circuit, it is ok to use smaller wire sizes than normal power circuits such as:

Possible Choices:

awg 16 wires

awg 18 wires

awg 16 and 18 wires

It is not ok to do so.

Answer:

On a Class 1 Circuit, it is ok to use smaller wire sizes than normal power circuits such as No. 16 and No. 18 AWG conductors but they have to be insulated for 600 volts and they have to be protected.

Question 33:

Class 1 signaling and remote control circuits are limited to:

Possible Choices:

150V

300V

400v

600V

Answer:

Class 1 signaling and remote control circuits are limited to max 600 volts.

Question 34:

When a circuit controls equipment can introduce a direct life safety hazard, the circuit has to be:

Possible Choices:

Class 1

Class 1 or 2

Class 2 or 3

Class 1, 2 or 3

Answer:

When a circuit controls equipment can introduce a direct life safety hazard, the circuit has to be Class 1 and NOT Class 2 NOR Class 3!

Question 35:

Class 2 circuits must be kept separate from lighting.

Possible Choices:

True

False

Answer:

True. Class 2 circuits must be kept separate from power and lighting and Class 1 circuits. Class 2 circuit and Class 3 circuit conductors should NOT be installed in an auxiliary gutter or wireway that has Class 1 circuit or power and lighting.

Question 36:

Generally, cables that are installed in ducts for environmental air should be of what type?

Possible Choices:

Type CL2P only.

Type CL3P only.

Type CL2P or CL3P.

Type CL2R or CL3R.

Answer:

Generally, cables that are installed in ducts, plenums, and other spaces for environmental air should be of Type CL2P or CL3P.

Question 37:

Cables installed in building locations other than in plenums for environmental air may be:

Possible Choices:

CL2 only

CL3 only

CL3P only

CL2R only

either CL2 or CL3

Answer:

Cables installed in building locations other than in plenums or ducts for environmental air may be either CL2 or CL3.

Question 38:

Voltage drop can be calculated based on:

Possible Choices:

Voltage drop = (the circuit length in ft.) x (resistance per 1 ft.)

Voltage drop = (2) x (the circuit length in ft.) x (resistance per 1 ft.)

Voltage drop = (3) x (the circuit length in ft.) x (resistance per 1 ft.) x (current)

Voltage drop = (2) x (the circuit length in ft.) x (resistance per 1 ft.) x (current / 0.5)

Voltage drop = (2) x (the circuit length in ft.) x (resistance per 1 ft.) x (current)

Answer:

Voltage drop is the volts lost due to resistance of wire: Voltage drop = (2) x (the circuit length in ft.) x (resistance per 1 ft.) x (current)

Question 39:

Class 2 circuits:

Possible Choices:

may be derived from a larger transformer by using fuses.

may not be derived from a larger transformer by using fuses.

Answer:

Class 2 circuits may not be derived from a larger transformer by using fuses.

Question 40:

The pulling tension in pounds for a copper wire should not exceed how many times the circular mil area of a conductor?

Possible Choices:

0.008

0.08

0.8

1.2

0.12

0.012

Answer:

The pulling tension in pounds for a copper wire should not exceed .008 times the circular mil area of a conductor.

Question 1:

The breaking capacity specifies:

Possible Choices:

the minimum current the fuse can handle.

the maximum current the fuse can handle.

Answer:

The breaking capacity specifies the maximum current the fuse can handle.

Question 2:

_____ occurs when there are two points in the circuit accidentally coming in contact.

Possible Choices:

Short circuit

Long circuit

Over current

Low voltage

Answer:

Short circuit occurs when there are two points in the circuit accidentally coming in contact, causing unwanted current flow between them.

Question 3:

Circuits of 30 A may be used to serve fixed lighting units with heavy-duty lampholders in non-dwellings units.

Possible Choices:

True

False

Answer:

True. Circuits of 30 A may be used to serve fixed lighting units with heavy-duty lampholders or appliances in non-dwellings units.

Question 4:

Circuits of 40 A may be used to serve fixed lighting with heavy-duty lampholders in fixed cooking appliances.

Possible Choices:

True

False

Answer:

True. Circuits of 40 or 50 A may be used to serve fixed lighting with heavy-duty lampholders in fixed cooking appliances, infrared heating units or heavy-duty appliances in non-dwellings units.

Question 5:

You need to have at least how many wall switch-controlled lighting outlets installed in every habitable room?

Possible Choices:

1

2

3

4

5

Answer:

You need to have at least one wall switch-controlled lighting outlet installed in every habitable room and bathroom.

Question 6:

A lighting system that has an isolating power supply operating at no more than ____ volts peak under any load condition is considered as low voltage

Possible Choices:

20

30

40

50

60

Answer:

A lighting system that has an isolating power supply operating at no more than 30 volts or 42.4 volts peak under any load condition and with its secondary circuits limited to 25 amp max is considered as low voltage and is practically/relatively safe from contact and may not always need grounding unless some other factors come into play.

Question 7:

For both power-limited and non-power-limited circuits, surge protective devices can be considered for protecting against electrical surges.

Possible Choices:

True

False

Answer:

True. For both power-limited and non-power-limited circuits, surge protective devices can be considered for protecting against electrical surges.

Question 8:

When installing surge protective devices to protect the circuits, the requirements of NEC Article _____ need to be followed.

Possible Choices:

285

300

500

600

800

Answer:

When installing surge protective devices to protect the circuits, the requirements of NEC Article 285 need to be followed.

Question 9:

FPL cables may be used for general purpose alarms without conduit. Exceptions include (choose all that apply):

Possible Choices:

riser

duct

plenum applications

There are no exceptions at all.

Answer:

FPL cables may be used for general purpose alarms without conduit. Exceptions include: riser, duct, and plenum applications.

Question 10:

_____ are limited energy cables suitable to be installed in environmental air plenum spaces without conduit.

Possible Choices:

FPL

FPLP

FPLR

FPLC

FPLA

Answer:

FPLP are limited energy cables suitable to be installed in environmental air plenum spaces without conduit.

Question 11:

_____ are limited energy cables suitable to be installed in vertical riser shafts without conduit.

Possible Choices:

FPL

FPLP

FPLR

FPLC

FPLA

Answer:

FPLR are limited energy cables suitable to be installed in vertical riser shafts without conduit.

Question 12:

Before the cable conductors are terminated they must first be tested on (choose all that apply):

Possible Choices:

stray voltages

ground faults

short circuit faults

resistance.

Answer:

According to NFPA Standard 72, before the cable conductors are terminated they must first be tested to verify suitability for operation. The tests necessary include stray voltages, ground faults, short circuit faults, and resistance.

Question 13:

_____ refers to any enclosed wiring method.

Possible Choices:

Raceway

Driveway

Runway

Wireway

Answer:

Raceway refers to any enclosed wiring method, which may include conduit and tubing in addition to other methods.

Question 14:

What are the valid types of conduit (choose all that apply)?

Possible Choices:

EMT

PVC

Flexible

Water

Answer:

Conduit may be metal (EMT), plastic (PVC), or flexible. They have different limitations on the maximum number of electrical wires allowed.

Question 15:

PVC conduit can hold many wires.

Possible Choices:

True

False

Answer:

PVC is a plastic conduit. It is thicker so it can hold fewer wires.

Question 16:

EMT conduit:

Possible Choices:

is a metal thin walled conduit.

is obsolete.

is too costly for normal use.

is banned in many states.

Answer:

EMT conduit is a metal thin walled conduit.

Question 17:

Flexible conduit is made of twisted metal, which is:

Possible Choices:

very easy to work with and can offer good protection.

very easy to work with but can offer less protection.

Answer:

Flexible conduit is made of twisted metal, which is very easy to work with but can offer less protection.

Question 18:

Intermediate metal conduit IMC is a:

Possible Choices:

circular metal raceway.

copper raceway.

costly metal raceway.

Answer:

Intermediate metal conduit IMC is a circular metal raceway. It is lighter and less costly than rigid metal conduit as it is often made of steel alloy.

Question 19:

Liquid-tight flexible metal conduit LFMC is a flexible raceway which has:

Possible Choices:

inner liquid-tight thermoplastic

outer liquid-tight thermoplastic

special shielding around the wires

Answer:

Liquid-tight flexible metal conduit LFMC is a flexible raceway which has a layer of outer liquid-tight thermoplastic for covering and protecting the conductors from moisture and corrosives.

Question 20:

You want to know that metal conduit can technically act in place of the green grounding wire if:

Possible Choices:

non-metal boxes are being used with it.

metal boxes are being used with it.

voltage is under 30V.

voltage is under 50V.

Answer:

You want to know that metal conduit can technically act in place of the green grounding wire if metal boxes are being used with it.

Question 21:

_____ wireways are preferred when there is a need to, within the raceway, make terminations, splices, or taps to several devices.

Possible Choices:

Metal

Plastic

PVC

Answer:

Metal wireways are preferred when there is a need to, within the raceway, make terminations, splices, or taps to several devices.

Question 22:

A Separately Derived System may refer to (choose all possible answers):

Possible Choices:

a premises wiring system with power derived from a battery

a premises wiring system with power derived from a solar system

a premises wiring system with power derived from a generator

Answer:

A Separately Derived System refers to a premises wiring system with power derived from another source, such as a battery, a solar system, or a generator ...etc. This system does not have any direct electrical connection or any solidly connected grounded circuit conductor to those supply conductors originating in another system.

Question 23:

You may want to avoid using solid conductors for flexible connections.

Answer:

True. Avoid using solid conductors for flexible connections. When flexibility is needed, use flexible stranded conductors, together with flexible raceways, especially for those connections to motors and similar equipments.

Question 24:

When installing a DC system, it is not a requirement to provide a grounding electrode system with a grounding electrode conductor.

Possible Choices:

True

False

Answer:

False. When installing a DC system, you need to provide a grounding electrode system with a grounding electrode conductor. You may use a common DC grounding-electrode conductor to serve multiple inverters assuming the common grounding electrode and the tap conductors are properly sized.

Question 25:

ARTICLE ___ covers circuits and equipments that operate at 50 volts or less.

Possible Choices:

520

620

720

820

There is no such article.

Answer:

ARTICLE 720 covers circuits and equipments that operate at 50 volts or less.

Question 26:

For a low voltage configuration, the conductors to use should never be smaller than:

Possible Choices:

10 AWG

12 AWG

14 AWG

16 AWG

18 AWG

Answer:

For a low voltage configuration, the conductors to use should never be smaller than 12 AWG copper (or equivalent).

Question 27:

For a low voltage configuration, the conductors to use for appliance branch circuits that supply more than one appliance should never be smaller than:

Possible Choices:

10 AWG

12 AWG

14 AWG

16 AWG

18 AWG

Answer:

For a low voltage configuration, the conductors to use for appliance branch circuits that supply more than one appliance should never be smaller than 10 AWG copper (or equivalent).

Question 28:

For a low voltage configuration, standard lampholders with a rating less than _____ watts should not be used.

Possible Choices:

220

300

500

660

800

Answer:

For a low voltage configuration, standard lampholders with a rating less than 660 watts should not be used.

Question 29:

Even in a low voltage configuration, the receptacles of less than ___-ampere rating should not be used in kitchens where portable appliances will be deployed.

Possible Choices:

20

30

40

50

60

Answer:

Even in a low voltage configuration, the receptacles of less than 20-ampere rating should not be used in kitchens where portable appliances will be deployed.

Question 30:

Even in a low voltage configuration, the receptacles of less than _____-ampere rating should not be used in laundries where portable appliances will be deployed.

Possible Choices:

20

30

40

50

60

Answer:

Even in a low voltage configuration, the receptacles of less than 20-ampere rating should not be used in laundries where portable appliances will be deployed.

Question 1:

Even in a low voltage configuration, cables should be supported by:

Possible Choices:

shielding.

the raceway.

metallic enclosure.

the building structure.

Answer:

Even in a low voltage configuration, cables should be supported by the building structure.

Question 2:

A Class 1 Circuit stays between:

<u>Possible Choices:</u>

the load side of the overcurrent device and the connected equipment.

the supply side of the overcurrent device and the building entrance.

the load side of the overcurrent device and the building exit.

the supply side of the overcurrent device and the fuse..

Answer:

A Class 1 Circuit stays between the load side of the overcurrent device and the connected equipment.

Question 3:

Whenever practicable, communications wires and cables should be located _____ electric light or power conductors.

Possible Choices:

Below

above

Answer:

Whenever practicable, communications wires and cables should be located below electric light or power conductors.

Question 4:

You should not allow communications wires to be attached to a cross-arm if:

Possible Choices:

the cross-arm carries electric power conductors.

the cross-arm carries no electric power conductors.

the area has moisture.

Answer:

You should not allow communications wires to be attached to a cross-arm if the cross-arm carries electric power conductors.

Question 5:

At the roof, you need to give your communications cables a minimum vertical clearance of ___ feet from the points above which they pass.

Possible Choices:

4

5

6

7

8

9

10

Answer:

At the roof, you need to give your communications cables a minimum vertical clearance of 8 feet from the points above which they pass.

Question 6:

A Class ___ Circuit stays between the load side of a Class 2 power source and a connected equipment.

Possible Choices:

1

2

3

4

5

Answer:

A Class 2 Circuit stays between the load side of a Class 2 power source and a connected equipment.

Question 7:

Remote-control circuits for use with safety-control equipments are considered Class ___ if failure to operate can introduce direct fire or life hazard.

Possible Choices:

1

2

3

4

5

Answer:

Remote-control circuits for use with safety-control equipments are considered Class 1 if failure to operate can introduce direct fire or life hazard.

Question 8:

Class 1 Power-Limited Circuits should be supplied from a source that has a rated output of _____ volts or below only.

Possible Choices:

20

30

40

50

60

Answer:

Class 1 Power-Limited Circuits should be supplied from a source that has a rated output of 30 volts or below only.

Question 9:

A Class ___ circuit always considers safety from a fire initiation standpoint.

Possible Choices:

1

2

3

4

5

Answer:

A Class 2 circuit always considers safety from a fire initiation standpoint.

Question 10:

Class 1 Power Sources other than transformers should have protection from overcurrent devices rated at max _____ of the volt-ampere rating of the source divided by the rated voltage.

<u>Possible Choices:</u>

120%

130%

157%

167%

187%

Answer:

Class 1 Power Sources other than transformers should have protection from overcurrent devices rated at max 167% of the volt-ampere rating of the source divided by the rated voltage.

Question 11:

A Class ___ circuit permits higher voltage than a Class 2 circuit.

Possible Choices:

1

3

Answer:

A Class 3 circuit permits higher voltage than a Class 2 circuit.

Question 12:

____ refers to the max volt-ampere output after a single minute of operation disregarding load and overcurrent protection.

Possible Choices:

EAmax

RAmax

ZAmax

VAmax

Imax

Answer:

VAmax refers to the max volt-ampere output after a single minute of operation disregarding load and overcurrent protection.

Question 13:

_____ refers to the max output current under any noncapacitive load and with overcurrent protection skipped.

Possible Choices:

EAmax

RAmax

ZAmax

VAmax

Imax

Answer:

Imax refers to the max output current under any noncapacitive load and with overcurrent protection skipped.

Question 14:

Class 1 Remote-Control and Signaling Circuits should never exceed:

Possible Choices:

50 volts.

60 volts.

500 volts.

600 volts.

Answer:

Class 1 Remote-Control and Signaling Circuits should never exceed 600 volts.

Question 15:

A Class 3 circuit always considers safety from a fire initiation standpoint.

Possible Choices:

True

False

Answer:

A Class 3 circuit always considers safety from a fire initiation standpoint.

Question 16:

Cables and conductors of Class 2 and Class 3 circuits should not be placed in a cable tray with conductors of electric light.

<u>*Possible Choices:*</u>

True

False

Answer:

True. Cables and conductors of Class 2 and Class 3 circuits should not be placed in a cable tray with conductors of electric light.

Question 17:

Any accessible portion of abandoned Class 2 cables:

Possible Choices:

should be removed.

may be retained.

should be labeled.

Answer:

Any accessible portion of abandoned Class 2 cables should be removed.

Question 18:

The power output of the source of Class 1 Remote-Control and Signaling Circuits:

Possible Choices:

are required to be limited.

are NOT required to be limited.

Answer:

The power output of the source of Class 1 Remote-Control and Signaling Circuits are NOT required to be limited.

Question 19:

Class 1 circuit conductors and power-supply conductors that are not functionally associated:

Possible Choices:

should be separated by a solid fixed barrier.

are not required to be separated by a solid fixed barrier.

Answer:

Class 1 circuit conductors and power-supply conductors that are not functionally associated should be separated by a solid fixed barrier.

Question 20:

Class 1 circuits may occupy the same cable as long as:

Possible Choices:

all conductors are insulated for the max voltage of any conductor in the same cable.

all conductors are insulated for the min voltage of any conductor in the same cable.

all conductors are insulated for the max voltage x 150% of any conductor in the same cable.

all conductors are insulated for the max voltage x 167% of any conductor in the same cable.

Answer:

Class 1 circuits may occupy the same cable (AC or DC does not matter) as long as all conductors are insulated for the max voltage of any conductor in the same cable.

Question 21:

Class 1 and Class 2 circuits should be identified at terminal and junction locations.

Possible Choices:

True

False

Answer:

True. Class 1 and Class 2 circuits should be identified at terminal and junction locations.

Question 22:

Overcurrent protection should never exceed ____ amperes for 18 AWG conductors.

Possible Choices:

5

6

7

8

9

10

12

Answer:

Overcurrent protection should never exceed 7 amperes for 18 AWG conductors.

Question 23:

Class 1 circuit conductors are normally allowed to be tapped.

Possible Choices:

True

False

Answer:

True. Class 1 circuit conductors are normally allowed to be tapped.

Question 24:

Overcurrent protection should never exceed ___ amperes for 16 AWG.

Possible Choices:

5

6

7

8

9

10

12

Answer:

Overcurrent protection should never exceed 10 amperes for 16 AWG.

Question 25:

Class 1 circuits and power-supply circuits may stay in the same raceway if:

Possible Choices:

the equipment powered is functionally associated.

the equipment powered is not functionally associated.

the equipment powered is less than 30V.

the equipment powered is less than 50V.

the equipment powered is less than 60V.

Answer:

Class 1 circuits and power-supply circuits may stay in the same raceway if and only if the equipment powered is functionally associated.

Question 26:

Supply service drops of max 750 volts that run parallel to communications service drops should possess a minimum separation of _____ inches at any point along the span.

Possible Choices:

1

3

6

8

10

12

Answer:

Supply service drops of max 750 volts that run parallel to communications service drops should possess a minimum separation of 12 inches at any point along the span.

Question 27:

Talking about the definition of Imax:

Possible Choices:

this definition does not include short circuit.

this definition does not exclude short circuit.

Answer:

Imax refers to the max output current under any noncapacitive load – this definition does not exclude short circuit.

Question 28:

Cables and conductors of Class 2 circuits may be placed in a cable compartment with conductors of non-power-limited fire alarm circuits.

Possible Choices:

True

False

Answer:

False. Cables and conductors of Class 2 and Class 3 circuits should not be placed in a cable compartment with conductors of non-power-limited fire alarm circuits.

Question 29:

The length of an unlisted outside plant cable should be limited to ___ feet.

Possible Choices:

20

30

40

50

60

Answer:

The length of an unlisted outside plant cable should be limited to 50 feet.

Question 30:

A primary protector should be located as close as practicable to where the cable enters the building.

Possible Choices:

True

False

It depends on the size of the protector.

It depends on the capacity of the protector.

Answer:

True. A primary protector should be located as close as practicable to where the cable enters the building.

Question 1:

With a primary protector installed inside a building, the communications wires should enter the building through:

Possible Choices:

bushing

drip loop

protector

OCPD

Answer:

With a primary protector installed inside a building, the communications wires should enter the building through a noncombustible nonabsorbent insulating bushing (or a metal raceway).

Question 2:

Raceways or bushings that enter a building should be:

Possible Choices:

sloped upward from the inside

sloped upward from the outside

completely vertical

Answer:

Raceways or bushings that enter a building should be sloped upward from the outside or with drip loops formed.

Question 3:

Whenever practicable, a distance of ___ feet or more should be maintained between communications wires and lightning conductors.

Possible Choices:

4

5

6

7

8

Answer:

Whenever practicable, a distance of 6 feet or more should be maintained between communications wires and lightning conductors.

Question 4:

Only plastic splice cases may be used as enclosures for terminating telephone cables.

Possible Choices:

True

False

Answer:

False. Splice (plastic/metal) cases may be used as enclosures for terminating telephone cables.

Question 5:

Cables and conductors of Class 3 circuits should not be placed in a cable compartment with conductors of non-power-limited fire alarm circuits.

Possible Choices:

True

False

Answer:

True. Cables and conductors of Class 2 and Class 3 circuits should not be placed in a cable compartment with conductors of non-power-limited fire alarm circuits.

Question 6:

The bonding conductor for use with the primary protector should never be smaller than _____ AWG.

Possible Choices:

11

12

13

14

15

16

Answer:

The bonding conductor for use with the primary protector should never be smaller than 14 AWG.

Question 7:

Secondary protectors on those circuits exposed to possible accidental contact with electric light conductors of _____ volts to ground should be used with primary protectors.

Possible Choices:

50+

120+

200+

220+

300+

Answer:

Secondary protectors on those circuits exposed to possible accidental contact with electric light conductors of 300+ volts to ground should be used with primary protectors.

Question 8:

Whenever there is lightning exposure, the interbuilding circuit must be protected:

Possible Choices:

by a listed primary protector on each end.

by a listed primary or secondary protector on each end.

by a listed primary protector on at least one end.

by a listed primary or secondary protector on at least one end.

Answer:

Whenever there is lightning exposure, the interbuilding circuit must be protected by a listed primary protector on each end.

Question 9:

An area with an average of __ or less thunderstorm days a year plus an earth resistivity of fewer than __ ohmmeters is not considered to have lightning exposure.

Possible Choices:

5/100

3/100

10/200

10/300

12/800

Answer:

An area with an average of 5 or less thunderstorm days a year plus an earth resistivity of fewer than 100 ohmmeters is not considered to have lightning exposure.

Question 10:

The fire alarm circuit disconnect should be designed in such a way that it can be secured in the "on" position.

Possible Choices:

True

False

Answer:

True. The fire alarm circuit disconnect should be designed in such a way that it can be secured in the "on" position.

Question 11:

Concerning fire alarm systems, the overcurrent protection should not exceed _____ amperes for 18 AWG conductors.

Possible Choices:

5

6

7

8

9

10

Answer:

Concerning fire alarm systems, the overcurrent protection should not exceed 7 amperes for 18 AWG conductors.

Question 12:

The location of the branch-circuit overcurrent protective device for supplying fire alarm equipments must be permanently identified at the fire alarm control unit.

Possible Choices:

True

False

It depends on the type of building.

It depends on the size of building.

Answer:

The location of the branch-circuit overcurrent protective device for supplying fire alarm equipments must be permanently identified at the fire alarm control unit.

Question 13:

The fire alarm circuit disconnecting means should have _____ identification.

Possible Choices:

red

green

yellow

orange

Answer:

The fire alarm circuit disconnecting means should have red identification.

Question 14:

The power source of non-powerlimited fire alarm circuits should have an output voltage no larger than _____ volts nominal.

Possible Choices:

200

300

400

500

600

700

800

Answer:

The power source of non-powerlimited fire alarm circuits should have an output voltage no larger than 600 volts nominal.

Question 15:

The branch circuit for supplying fire alarm equipments is normally allowed to supply other loads.

Possible Choices:

True

False

Answer:

False. The branch circuit for supplying fire alarm equipments should not be used to supply other loads.

Question 16:

Power-supply and fire alarm circuit conductors may stay in the same cable as long as:

Possible Choices:

they are connected to the same equipment.

they are not connected to the same equipment.

they should never stay in the same cable no matter what.

Answer:

Power-supply and fire alarm circuit conductors may stay in the same cable as long as they are connected to the same equipment.

Question 17:

Only metallic terminal boxes may be used as enclosures for splicing telephone cables.

Possible Choices:

True

False

Answer:

False. Terminal boxes (plastic/metal) may be used as enclosures for splicing telephone cables.

Question 18:

You can only use copper conductors for fire alarm systems.

Possible Choices:

True

False

Answer:

True. You can only use copper conductors for fire alarm systems.

Question 19:

The proper size of conductors in a multiconductor cable should be at least:

Possible Choices:

12 AWG.

14 AWG.

16 AWG.

18 AWG.

26 AWG.

Answer:

The proper size of conductors in a multiconductor cable should be at least 26 AWG.

Question 20:

The proper size of single conductors should be at least:

Possible Choices:

12 AWG.

14 AWG.

16 AWG.

18 AWG.

26 AWG.

Answer:

The proper size of single conductors should be at least 18 AWG.

Question 21:

A cable that is low smoke-producing should exhibit a max peak optical density of no more than:

Possible Choices:

0.5.

0.7.

0.8.

0.9.

1.2.

Answer:

A cable that is low smoke-producing should exhibit a max peak optical density of no more than 0.5.

Question 22:

Direct-buried cables that are emerging from the ground must be protected by enclosures or other means.

Possible Choices:

True

False

Answer:

True. Direct-buried cables that are emerging from the ground must be protected by enclosures or other means.

Question 23:

Primary electrical protections are necessary on aerial network-powered broadband communications conductors:

Possible Choices:

that are not grounded or interrupted.

that are grounded or interrupted.

that are not grounded or non-interrupted.

that are enclosed in metal enclosure only.

that are not enclosed in metal enclosure only.

Answer:

Primary electrical protections are necessary on aerial network-powered broadband communications conductors that are not grounded or interrupted.

Question 24:

A cable that is fire resistant should exhibit a max flame spread distance of no more than _____ feet.

Possible Choices:

4

5

6

7

8

9

Answer:

A cable that is fire resistant should exhibit a max flame spread distance of 5 feet only.

Question 25:

Primary electrical protections are necessary on underground network-powered broadband communications conductors:

Possible Choices:

that are not grounded or interrupted.

that are grounded or interrupted.

that are not grounded or non-interrupted.

that are enclosed in plastic enclosure only.

that are not enclosed in plastic enclosure only.

Answer:

Primary electrical protections are necessary on underground network-powered broadband communications conductors that are not grounded or interrupted.

Question 26:

On those network-powered broadband communications conductors that are not exposed to lightning, you do not need to provide primary electrical protection.

Possible Choices:

True

False

Answer:

False. On those network-powered broadband communications conductors that are not exposed to lightning, you should still provide primary electrical protection.

Question 27:

Fuseless-type primary protectors are never allowed.

Possible Choices:

True

False

Answer:

False. Fuseless-type primary protectors may be used when power fault currents on the protected conductors along the cable are all safely limited.

Question 28:

Hot water pipes may be used as grounding electrodes for the protectors.

Possible Choices:

True

False

Answer:

False. Hot/steam water pipes should not be used as grounding electrodes for the protectors.

Question 29:

A bonding jumper at least ____ AWG copper in size should be used to connect the network-powered broadband communications system grounding electrode with the power grounding electrode system.

Possible Choices:

6

8

9

10

12

14

16

Answer:

A bonding jumper at least 6 AWG copper in size should be used to connect the network-powered broadband communications system grounding electrode with the power grounding electrode system.

Question 30:

Concerning fire alarm systems, the overcurrent protection should not exceed ___ amperes for 16 AWG conductors.

Possible Choices:

8

10

20

30

50

60

Answer:

Concerning fire alarm systems, the overcurrent protection should not exceed 10 amperes for 16 AWG conductors.

Question 1:

You should not allow medium-power network-powered broadband communications cables to stay in the same cable tray with Class 2 and Class 3 remote-control circuits.

Possible Choices:

True

False

True only if the cables are longer than 50 feet.

True only if the cables are longer than 60 feet.

True only if the cables are longer than 100 feet.

Answer:

True. You should not allow medium-power network-powered broadband communications cables to stay in the same cable tray with Class 2 and Class 3 remote-control circuits.

Question 2:

Bends in network broadband cable are NEVER allowed.

Possible Choices:

True

False

True only if the cables are longer than 50 feet.

True only if the cables are longer than 60 feet.

True only if the cables are longer than 100 feet.

Answer:

False. Bends in network broadband cable are allowed but you need to make sure damages are not made to the cable.

Question 3:

In an assembled cable that contains a jacketed combination of coaxial cable and multiple individual conductors, insulation for each individual conductor has to be rated for ____ volts at the least.

Possible Choices:

200

300

400

500

600

Answer:

In an assembled cable that contains a jacketed combination of coaxial cable and multiple individual conductors, insulation for each individual conductor has to be rated for 300 volts at the least.

Question 4:

Which of the following is a device that converts optical signal into component signals such as voice, audio, video, data ...etc?

Possible Choices:

RDT

ONT

SNT

FNT

CATV

CCTV

Answer:

Optical Network Terminal ONT is a device that converts optical signal into component signals such as voice, audio, video, data ...etc.

Question 5:

It is ARTICLE _____ that specifically covers PREMISES-POWERED BROADBAND COMMUNICATIONS SYSTEMS.

Possible Choices:

810

820

830

840

850

Answer:

It is ARTICLE 840 that covers PREMISES-POWERED BROADBAND COMMUNICATIONS SYSTEMS.

Question 6:

When you pull three conductors cables into a raceway, jamming may occur when the ratio of the inside diameter of the raceway to the outside diameter of the cable is in the range of:

Possible Choices:

2.8 to 3.2.

3.8 to 4.2.

5.8 to 6.2.

7.8 to 8.2.

having only three cables should hardly jam anything.

Answer:

When you pull three conductors cables into a raceway, jamming may occur when the ratio of the inside diameter of the raceway to the outside diameter of the cable is in the range of 2.8 to 3.2.

Question 7:

A flexible cord of 2+ conductors may be treated as a single conductor for purpose of:

Possible Choices:

calculating the conduit fill area.

fire prevention.

tension strength check.

security.

Answer:

A flexible cord of 2+ conductors may be treated as a single conductor for purpose of calculating the percentage conduit fill area.

Question 8:

Generally, overcurrent devices should not be interchangeable with devices of higher ratings.

Possible Choices:

True

False

Answer:

True. Generally, overcurrent devices should not be interchangeable with devices of higher ratings.

Question 9:

What tells the heat transfer capability through a substance by conduction?

Possible Choices:

Thermal resistivity

Weather resistivity

Pressure resistivity

Answer:

Thermal resistivity tells the heat transfer capability through a substance by conduction.

Question 10:

A _____ is the area of demarcation between intra-building and inter-building cabling.

Possible Choices:

RDF

CDF

FDF

MDF

Answer:

A Main Distribution Frame MDF is the area of demarcation between intra-building and inter-building cabling (where they are connected).

Question 11:

Which of the following is a device or circuit that extends community antenna television systems from the ONT of the service provider to the customer equipment?

Possible Choices:

RDT

ONT

SNT

FNT

CATV

CCTV

Answer:

A Premises Community Antenna Television CATV Circuit extends community antenna television systems from the ONT of the service provider to the customer equipment.

Question 12:

The construction of MDF must be completed AFTER you install the communications cables.

<u>Possible Choices:</u>

True

False

Answer:

False. The construction of MDF must be completed before you can install the communications cables.

Question 13:

Thermal resistivity is typically expressed in the units of:

Possible Choices:

°C-cm/watt.

°C-mm/Kwatt.

°C-cm/Hz.

°C-cm/volt.

Answer:

Thermal resistivity is expressed in the units of °C-cm/watt.

Question 14:

_____ is what serves as the demarcation point for voice, data, video ...etc.

Possible Choices:

RDF

GDF

IDF

VDF

Answer:

An Intermediate Distribution Frame IDF is what serves as the demarcation point for voice, data, video ...etc.

Question 15:

All communication cable bundles should make use of an enclosed fire rated pathway device if the cables have to penetrate the rated walls.

Possible Choices:

True

False

True only for voice cables.

True only for video cables.

Answer:

True. All communication cable bundles should make use of an enclosed fire rated pathway device if the cables have to penetrate the rated walls.

Question 16:

A Class __ Division __ Location is one with ignitable concentrations of flammable gases or vapors exist under normal operating conditions; that ignitable concentrations of such gases or vapors may exist frequently because of repair or maintenance operations or because of leakage.

Possible Choices:

I, 1

I, 2

II, 1

II, 2

III, 1

III, 2

Answer:

A Class I, Division 1 Location is one with ignitable concentrations of flammable gases or vapors exist under normal operating conditions; that ignitable concentrations of such gases or vapors may exist frequently because of repair or maintenance operations or because of leakage.

Question 17:

A Class __, Division __ Location is one with combustible dust not normally in the air in quantities sufficient to produce explosive or ignitable mixtures and dust accumulations are normally insufficient to interfere with the normal operation of electrical equipment or other apparatus.

.

Possible Choices:

I, 1

I, 2

II, 1

II, 2

III, 1

III, 2

Answer:

A Class II, Division 2 Location is one with combustible dust not normally in the air in quantities sufficient to produce explosive or ignitable mixtures and dust accumulations are normally insufficient to interfere with the normal operation of electrical equipment or other apparatus.

Question 18:

A Class ___ enclosure must be strong enough to contain an explosion within.

Possible Choices:

I

II

III

IV

Answer:

A Class I enclosure must be strong enough to contain an explosion within.

Question 19:

Class I, Division 1 equipment is often being referred to as:

Possible Choices:

explosion-proof.

water-proof.

moisture-proof.

dust-ignition proof.

Answer:

Class I, Division 1 equipment is often being referred to as explosion-proof.

Question 20:

Class II equipment is often called:

Possible Choices:

explosion-proof.

water-proof.

moisture-proof.

dust-ignition proof.

Answer:

Class II equipment is often called dust-ignition proof. It must seal out dust yet allows for a dust blanket.

Question 21:

Power-Limited Class 1 is always limited to 30V and 1,200VA.

Possible Choices:

True

False

Answer:

False. There are power limitations imposed on Class 1 circuits to ensure that the electrical energy carried by the circuit remains within safe levels. These power limitations help prevent overheating of conductors and components, reducing the risk of fire Power-Limited Class 1 is either an AC or DC circuit. The circuit is supplied by a power source that is limited to 30V and 1,000VA.

Question 22:

Class 1 remote control circuits and signaling circuits can operate up to ____V with no ampere limitation.

Possible Choices:

220

300

380

400

600

Answer:

Class 1 remote control circuits and signaling circuits can operate up to 600V with no ampere limitation. Class 1 circuits are commonly used in various applications where safety is paramount, including low-voltage lighting systems, control circuits, communication systems, and instrumentation circuits.

Question 23:

Class __ circuits cover mostly everything to be installed in the security industry.

Possible Choices:

1

2

3

4

5

Answer:

Class 2 circuits are designed for safety from fire ignition and electrical shock and cover mostly everything to be installed in the security industry.

Question 24:

You should try to maintain a separation of at least __ feet between your network-powered broadband communications cable and any lightning conductors.

Possible Choices:

6

7

8

9

12

14

Answer:

You should try to maintain a separation of at least 6 feet between your network-powered broadband communications cable and any lightning conductors.

Question 25:

Your network-powered broadband communications cables that are attached to the building structure located within _____ feet of finished grade should be protected by raceways.

Possible Choices:

6

7

8

9

12

14

Answer:

Your network-powered broadband communications cables that are attached to the building structure located within 8 feet of finished grade should be protected by raceways or other means.

Question 26:

Your direct-buried network-powered broadband communications cables should not need to be separated from conductors of any non-power limited fire alarm circuit conductors.

Possible Choices:

True

False

Answer:

False. Your direct-buried network-powered broadband communications cables should be separated from conductors of any non-power limited fire alarm circuit conductors.

Question 27:

Overhead spans of your network-powered broadband communications cables should stay at least _____ feet above the sidewalk.

Possible Choices:

7.5

8.5

9.5

10.5

12.5

Answer:

Overhead spans of your network-powered broadband communications cables should stay at least 9.5 feet above finished grade or the sidewalk.

Question 28:

Installing network-powered broadband cables in hollow space should be done to:

Possible Choices:

not increase the possible spread of fire.

prevent moisture.

reduce fire prevention cost.

Answer:

Installing network-powered broadband cables in hollow space should be done to not increase the possible spread of fire.

Question 29:

Medium-power network-powered broadband communications circuits that stay outside of a building should be installed using what cables (choose all that apply):

Possible Choices:

Type BMU

Type BM

Type BMR

Type BLU

Type BLX

Answer:

Medium-power network-powered broadband communications circuits that stay outside of a building should be installed using Type BMU, Type BM, or Type BMR cables.

Question 30:

Low-power network-powered broadband communications circuits located outside a building should be installed using what cables (choose all that apply):

Possible Choices:

Type BMC

Type BMX

Type BMD

Type BLU

Type BLX

Answer:

Low-power network-powered broadband communications circuits located outside a building should be installed using Type BLU or Type BLX cables.

Question 31:

Before attempting to perform any electrical installations, you are required by law at the federal law to first gather all drawings regarding the subject.

Possible Choices:

True

False

Answer:

False. Before attempting to perform any electrical installations, you should first gather drawings, instructions and/or the relevant procedural documents regarding the subject. There is no mandatory federal law though.

Question 32:

The first thing to do when someone has suffered an electric shock is to:

call the fire stations.

call the police.

blow the fuse.

separate him from the currents.

Answer:

The first thing to do when someone has suffered an electric shock is to separate him from the currents.

Question 33:

Placing power cords or wires under carpets or rugs is not going to cause any problem.

Possible Choices:

True

False

Answer:

False. Placing power cords or wires under carpets or rugs is not recommended.

Question 34:

When digging in the ground, an accidental contact with underground wiring:

Possible Choices:

is never possible.

is of very low risk.

can be deadly.

Answer:

When digging in the ground, an accidental contact with underground wiring can be deadly.

Question 35:

According to OSHA, single conductors used as equipment grounding conductors should be No. ___ or larger.

Possible Choices:

3

4

5

6

7

8

Answer:

According to OSHA standard 1910.305(a)(3)(ii)(C), single conductors used as equipment grounding conductors should be No. 4 or larger.

Question 36:

According to OSHA, multiconductor cable exposed to direct sunshine needs to be identified as being sunlight resistant.

Possible Choices:

True

False

Answer:

True. According to OSHA standard 1910.305(a)(3)(ii)(D), multiconductor cable exposed to direct rays of the sun needs to be identified as being sunlight resistant.

Question 37:

According to OSHA, cable tray systems:

Possible Choices:

may be used in hoistways.

may ONLY be used in hoistways.

MUST be used in hoistways.

may NOT be used in hoistways.

None of the choices.

Answer:

According to OSHA standard 1910.305(a)(3)(v), cable tray systems may not be used in hoistways.

Question 38:

According to OSHA, receptacles you use:

Possible Choices:

should be of the grounding type.

should be of any type that is safe.

should be approved at the federal level.

Answer:

According to OSHA standard 1910.305(a)(2)(vi), receptacles you use should be of the grounding type.

Question 39:

According to OSHA, bare conductors:

Possible Choices:

may be used for wiring any temporary circuit under 600V.

may NOT be used for wiring any temporary circuit under 600V.

may be used for wiring any temporary circuit under 1000V.

may be used for wiring any temporary circuit under 1200V.

None of the choices.

Answer:

According to OSHA standard 1910.305(a)(2)(vii), bare conductors should not be used for wiring any temporary circuit.

Question 40:

According to OSHA, open conductors:

Possible Choices:

need to be separated from contact with walls and floors.

need NOT be separated from contact with walls and floors.

need to be separated from contact with walls but not floors.

need to be separated from contact with floors but not walls.

None of the choices.

Answer:

According to OSHA standard 1910.305(a)(4)(iv), open conductors need to be separated from contact with walls and floors.

Question 41:

Audio system voltages can reach max:

Possible Choices:

10VAC.

20VAC.

30VAC.

40VAC.

50VAC.

60VAC.

70VAC.

80VAC.

90VAC.

None of the choices.

Answer:

Audio system voltages can reach max 70VAC.

Question 42:

Power-Limited Class 1 may be supplied by a power source limited to:

12V and 1000VA.

24V and 1000VA.

30V and 1000VA.

48V and 1000VA.

12V and 2000VA.

24V and 2000VA.

30V and 2000VA.

48V and 2000VA.

Answer:

Power-Limited Class 1 may be AC or DC circuit, and may be supplied by a power source limited to 30V and 1000VA.

Question 43:

A Class 2 circuit can have a max voltage of (choose all that apply):

Possible Choices:

20V, 5A for a total of less than 100VA

21V to 30V, 3.3A for a total of less than 100VA

31V 150V, 0.005A for a total of less than 0.5VA.

20V, 10A for a total of less than 200VA

21V to 30V, 3.3A for a total of less than 500VA

31V 150V, 0.05A for a total of less than 1VA.

Answer:

A Class 2 circuit can have a max voltage of 20V, 5A for a total of less than 100VA; 21V to 30V, 3.3A for a total of less than 100VA; or 31V 150V, 0.005A for a total of less than 0.5VA.

Question 44:

Using a junction box to encapsulate a 120V AC wire connection to a 12-24V DC power converter:

Possible Choices:

is acceptable

is not acceptable

Answer:

Class 1 circuits and Class 2 circuits must be separated. It is technically ok to use a junction box to encapsulate a 120V AC wire connection to a 12-24V DC power converter.

Question 45:

NEC now requires that you install Class 2 and 3 in a raceway.

Possible Choices:

True

False

Answer:

False. NEC does not specifically require that you install Class 2 and 3 in a raceway.

Question 46:

Telephone systems with ringer can have voltage that reaches max:

Possible Choices:

10VAC.

20VAC.

30VAC.

40VAC.

50VAC.

60VAC.

70VAC.

80VAC.

90VAC.

None of the choices.

Answer:

Telephone systems with ringer can have voltage that reaches max 90VAC.

Question 47:

When you use a dry cell battery as a power source for a Class 2, the voltage must be:

Possible Choices:

12V or less.

18V or less.

24V or less.

30V or less.

60V or less.

Answer:

When you use a dry cell battery as a power source for a Class 2, the voltage must be 30V or less.

Question 48:

You can never install Class 2 and Class 3 circuits with Class 1, non-power-limited fire alarm circuits!

Possible Choices:

True

False

Answer:

False. If you want to install Class 2 and Class 3 circuits with Class 1, non-power-limited fire alarm circuits, you must separate them with a barrier.

Question 49:

If you want to mix Class 2 conductors with Class 3 conductors,

Possible Choices:

you will have to use Class 2 wiring methods for the Class 3 conductors.

you will have to use Class 3 wiring methods for the Class 2 conductors.

you cannot do this!

Answer:

If you want to mix Class 2 conductors with Class 3 conductors, you will have to use Class 3 wiring methods for the Class 2 conductors.

Question 50:

Class 1 circuits:

Possible Choices:

can be in the same cable with power supply circuits if the equipment powered is functionally associated with the Class 1 circuit.

can be in the same cable with power supply circuits if the equipment powered is not functionally associated with the Class 1 circuit.

can be in the same cable with power supply circuits if the equipment powered is not functional.

can NEVER be in the same cable with power supply circuits.

Answer:

Class 1 circuits can be in the same cable with power supply circuits if the equipment powered is functionally associated with the Class 1 circuit.

Question 51:

Low voltage thermostat wires:

Possible Choices:

do require a box.

do not require a box.

Answer:

Low voltage (12 or 24 volts, thermostat wires, doorbells, phone lines, network cables, coax cables, etc) do not require a box. However, for convenience and for future access it is an excellent idea to provide a box.

Question 52:

The maximum branch-circuit voltage drop will be _____ V in a 120 V system.

Possible Choices:

1.2

2.4

4.8

6.4

7.8

8.4

Answer:

Typical voltage drop figures are 2% for the branch circuits in addition to 1% to 2% for feeders. The maximum branch-circuit voltage drop will be 2.4 V in a 120 V system.

Question 53:

For low-voltage wires the recommended draw strength is around _____ pounds.

Possible Choices:

10

14

18

21

25

31

Answer:

Low-voltage wires should not be pulled in the same manner as electrical lines as they can be damaged by rough handling. The recommended draw strength is around 25 pounds only.

Question 54:

Low voltage wires should be installed minimum how many foot away from the dwelling's main electrical wires, running parallel with all the cabling?

Possible Choices:

1

2

3

4

5

6

Answer:

Low voltage wires should be installed minimum ONE foot away from the dwelling's main electrical wires, running parallel with all the cabling. Higher voltage on electrical cables can create signal interference that can potentially affect the data cables.

Question 55:

The voltage drop between the point of supply for the low voltage electrical installation and any point in that electrical installation should never exceed ____ % of the nominal voltage of the point of supply.

Possible Choices:

2

3

4

5

6

7

Answer:

The voltage drop between the point of supply for the low voltage electrical installation and any point in that electrical installation should never exceed 5 % of the nominal voltage of the point of supply.

Question 56:

Low voltage cables do not need to be in a conduit if it is:

Possible Choices:

part of an electrical installation.

NOT part of an electrical installation.

Answer:

Low voltage cables do not need to be in a conduit if it is NOT part of an electrical installation. Otherwise it needs to be in conduit. It is ok to have low voltage wiring methods strapped to an existing conduit.

Question 57:

The maximum branch-circuit voltage drop will be _____ V in a 240 V system.

Possible Choices:

1.2

2.4

4.8

5.6

7.8

Answer:

Typical voltage drop figures are 2% for the branch circuits in addition to 1% to 2% for feeders. The maximum branch-circuit voltage drop will be 4.8 V in a 240 V system.

Question 58:

What is capacitive reactance in an AC circuit?

Possible Choices:

Resistance to current flow

Ability to store electrical energy

Inductance of the circuit

Time delay in the circuit

Answer:

Capacitive reactance is the measure of a capacitor's ability to store and release electrical energy in an alternating current (A)circuit. It arises due to the opposition to the change in voltage across the capacitor, leading to the storage and release of energy as the voltage changes.

Question 59:

What does baud rate represent in digital communication?

Possible Choices:

Data transmission speed

Signal frequency range

Error correction capability

Noise tolerance level

Answer:

Baud rate refers to the number of signal changes (transitions) per second in a communication channel and is a measure of the rate at which data is transmitted. It indicates the speed at which data is sent over a communication link, usually expressed in bits per second (bps) or symbols per second.

Question 60:

What does rise time measure in electronics?

Possible Choices:

Time taken for a signal to transition from low to high

Time taken for a signal to transition from high to low

Duration of a signal's high state

Duration of a signal's low state

Answer:

Rise time is the time taken for a signal to transition from a low voltage level to a high voltage level, typically measured between 10% and 90% of the signal's final value. It is an important parameter in electronics, especially in digital systems, as it affects signal integrity and timing performance.

Question 61:

What does fall time measure in electronics?

Possible Choices:

Time taken for a signal to transition from low to high

Time taken for a signal to transition from high to low

Duration of a signal's high state

Duration of a signal's low state

Answer:

Fall time is the time taken for a signal to transition from a high voltage level to a low voltage level, typically measured between 90% and 10% of the signal's final value. It is a crucial parameter in electronics, particularly in digital systems, as it affects signal integrity and switching characteristics.

Question 62:

What is near-end crosstalk (NEXT) in telecommunications?

Possible Choices:

Interference at the receiver caused by signals transmitted on adjacent channels

Interference at the transmitter caused by signals reflected back from the transmission medium

Interference at the receiver caused by signals transmitted on the same channel

Interference at the transmitter caused by signals transmitted on adjacent channels

Answer:

Near-end crosstalk (NEXT) refers to the interference or coupling of signals transmitted on the same channel at the sending end, which affects the quality of the received signal. It occurs due to electromagnetic coupling between adjacent signal paths and can degrade signal integrity and data transmission performance.

Question 63:

What is far-end crosstalk (FEXT) in telecommunications?

Possible Choices:

Interference at the receiver caused by signals transmitted on adjacent channels

Interference at the transmitter caused by signals reflected back from the transmission medium

Interference at the receiver caused by signals transmitted on the same channel

Interference at the transmitter caused by signals transmitted on adjacent channels

Answer:

Far-end crosstalk (FEXT) refers to the interference or coupling of signals transmitted on adjacent channels at the receiving end of a communication link. It occurs due to electromagnetic coupling between signal paths and can affect the quality of the received signal, especially in high-speed data transmission systems.

Question 64:

Which modulation technique is known for its resilience to noise and interference?

Possible Choices:

Amplitude Modulation (AM)

Frequency Modulation (FM)

Phase Modulation (PM)

Pulse Amplitude Modulation (PAM)

Answer:

Frequency modulation (FM) is known for its resistance to amplitude variations due to noise, making it less susceptible to noise and interference compared to amplitude modulation (AM).

Question 65:

What modulation technique is commonly used in analog television broadcasting?

Possible Choices:

Amplitude Modulation (AM)

Frequency Modulation (FM)

Phase Modulation (PM)

Quadrature Amplitude Modulation (QAM)

Answer:

Analog television broadcasting commonly uses amplitude modulation (AM) to transmit video and audio signals over the airwaves.

Question 66:

What is the key characteristic of phase modulation (PM)?

Possible Choices:

Variation of the amplitude of the carrier signal

Variation of the frequency of the carrier signal

Variation of the phase of the carrier signal

Combination of amplitude and frequency variations

Answer:

Phase modulation (PM) involves varying the phase of the carrier signal in proportion to the message signal, resulting in the encoding of information.

Question 67:

What modulation technique is commonly used in digital communication systems such as Wi-Fi and Bluetooth?

Possible Choices:

Amplitude Modulation (AM)

Frequency Modulation (FM)

Phase Modulation (PM)

Quadrature Amplitude Modulation (QAM)

Answer:

Phase modulation (PM) is commonly used in digital communication systems like Wi-Fi and Bluetooth for its efficient use of bandwidth and resilience to noise.

Question 68:

Light pipes are often used for what purpose in optical communication?

Possible Choices:

Transmitting light signals over long distances

Amplifying light signals

Modulating light signals

Distributing light signals within a confined space

Answer:

Light pipes, also known as optical fibers or fiber optics, are commonly used in optical communication to transmit light signals over short distances and distribute them within confined spaces such as buildings or data centers.

Question 69:

In optical communication, what property of light is modulated to encode information?

Possible Choices:

Intensity

Wavelength

Speed

Polarization

Answer:

In optical communication, information is typically encoded by modulating the intensity (amplitude) of the light signal transmitted through optical fibers.

Question 70:

What is the primary advantage of frequency modulation (FM) over amplitude modulation (AM) in radio broadcasting?

Possible Choices:

Greater resistance to noise and interference

Simpler receiver design

Higher efficiency in bandwidth utilization

Longer range of transmission

None of these.

Answer:

Frequency modulation (FM) offers greater resistance to noise and interference compared to amplitude modulation (AM), making it preferable for high-fidelity audio transmission in radio broadcasting.

Question 71:

What modulation technique is commonly used in radar systems for target detection and tracking?

Possible Choices:

Amplitude Modulation (AM)

Frequency Modulation (FM)

Pulse Modulation

Phase Modulation (PM)

Answer:

Pulse modulation techniques, such as pulse amplitude modulation (PAM) or pulse position modulation (PPM), are commonly used in radar systems for their ability to accurately detect and track targets.

Question 72:

What modulation technique is used in digital subscriber line (DSL) technology for high-speed internet access over telephone lines?

Possible Choices:

Amplitude Modulation (AM)

Frequency Modulation (FM)

Phase Modulation (PM)

Quadrature Amplitude Modulation (QAM)

None of these.

Answer:

Quadrature Amplitude Modulation (QAM) is used in DSL technology to modulate digital data onto analog signals transmitted over telephone lines, enabling high-speed internet access.

Question 73:

What is the critical angle in the context of fiber optic cables?

Possible Choices:

The angle at which light enters the fiber optic cable

The angle at which light exits the fiber optic cable

The maximum angle at which light can enter the fiber optic cable for total internal reflection

The angle at which light is refracted within the fiber optic cable

Answer:

The critical angle is the maximum angle at which light can enter the core of a fiber optic cable for total internal reflection to occur. Beyond this angle, light will escape from the core, resulting in signal loss.

Question 74:

What materials typically constitute the core and cladding of a fiber optic cable, respectively?

Possible Choices:

Plastic core and glass cladding

Glass core and plastic cladding

Glass core and glass cladding

Plastic core and plastic cladding

None of these.

Answer:

In most fiber optic cables, the core is made of glass to facilitate light transmission, while the cladding surrounding the core is made of plastic to provide protection and maintain the light within the core through total internal reflection.

Question 75:

What is the function of the glass core in a fiber optic cable?

Possible Choices:

To provide flexibility

To protect the cable from environmental factors

To transmit light signals through total internal reflection

To increase signal attenuation

Answer:

The glass core of a fiber optic cable is designed to transmit light signals by confining them within the core through total internal reflection, ensuring minimal signal loss and efficient transmission.

Question 76:

What is the primary role of the cladding in a fiber optic cable?

Possible Choices:

To facilitate light transmission

To protect the core from damage

To increase signal attenuation

To amplify light signals

None of these.

Answer:

The cladding of a fiber optic cable serves to protect the core from damage and environmental factors while also maintaining the light within the core through total internal reflection.

Question 77:

What happens if light enters the fiber optic cable at an angle greater than the critical angle?

Possible Choices:

Total internal reflection occurs

Light is absorbed by the core

Light exits the core and travels through the cladding

Light is reflected back to the source

None of these.

Answer:

If light enters the fiber optic cable at an angle greater than the critical angle, it will exit the core and travel through the cladding, resulting in signal loss and reduced transmission efficiency.

Question 78:

How does the refractive index of the core compare to that of the cladding in a fiber optic cable?

Possible Choices:

The refractive index of the core is higher

The refractive index of the cladding is higher

Both have the same refractive index

The refractive index depends on the type of fiber optic cable

None of these.

Answer:

The refractive index of the core in a fiber optic cable is typically higher than that of the cladding to facilitate total internal reflection and minimize signal loss.

Question 79:

What property of the fiber optic cable determines its ability to transmit light signals over long distances without significant loss?

Possible Choices:

Core diameter

Cladding thickness

Refractive index

Attenuation coefficient

None of these.

Answer:

The attenuation coefficient of a fiber optic cable determines its ability to transmit light signals over long distances without significant loss. Lower attenuation coefficients result in more efficient transmission and longer transmission distances.

Question 80:

What type of fiber optic cable is typically used for long-distance telecommunications and high-speed data transmission?

Possible Choices:

Multimode fiber

Single-mode fiber

Plastic optical fiber

Graded-index fiber

None of these.

Answer:

Single-mode fiber optic cables are typically used for long-distance telecommunications and high-speed data transmission due to their low attenuation and ability to transmit light signals over long distances without dispersion.

Question 81:

What is the core diameter of a single-mode fiber optic cable typically?

Possible Choices:

Larger than the wavelength of light

Smaller than the wavelength of light

Equal to the wavelength of light

It depends on the application

None of these.

Answer:

The core diameter of a single-mode fiber optic cable is typically much smaller than the wavelength of light being transmitted, allowing only a single mode of light to propagate through the core.

Question 82:

Which type of fiber optic cable is more susceptible to modal dispersion?

Possible Choices:

Single-mode fiber

Multimode fiber

Plastic optical fiber

Graded-index fiber

None of these.

Answer:

Multimode fiber optic cables are more susceptible to modal dispersion due to their larger core diameter and the presence of multiple propagation modes, which can result in signal distortion and dispersion.

Question 83:

What is the typical refractive index of the core in a fiber optic cable?

Possible Choices:

Less than 1

Equal to 1

Greater than 1

It depends on the type of fiber optic cable

None of these.

Answer:

The refractive index of the core in a fiber optic cable is typically greater than 1 to ensure total internal reflection and efficient light transmission within the core.

Question 84:

What is the purpose of doping in the manufacturing of fiber optic cables?

Possible Choices:

To increase core diameter

To decrease core diameter

To modify the refractive index

To decrease signal attenuation

None of these.

Answer:

Doping is the process of intentionally adding impurities to the core material of a fiber optic cable to modify its refractive index, which can enhance light transmission properties and minimize signal attenuation.

Question 85:

What is the primary purpose of a buffer jacket in a fiber optic cable?

Possible Choices:

To provide mechanical protection to the core and cladding

To enhance light transmission efficiency

To facilitate signal amplification

To reduce signal attenuation

None of these.

Answer:

The buffer jacket of a fiber optic cable serves to provide mechanical protection to the delicate core and cladding, preventing damage from handling, bending, and environmental factors.

Question 86:

Which layer of a fiber optic cable serves as the outermost protective covering?

Possible Choices:

Core

Cladding

Buffer jacket

Outer jacket

None of these.

Answer:

The outer jacket of a fiber optic cable serves as the outermost protective covering, providing additional mechanical protection and insulation against environmental factors.

Question 87:

What property does the refractive index of a material describe?

Possible Choices:

The speed of light in the material

The angle of light refraction at the material's interface

The amount of light absorbed by the material

The degree of light polarization in the material

None of these.

Answer:

The refractive index of a material describes the degree to which light is bent or refracted as it passes from one medium to another, determined by the ratio of the speed of light in a vacuum to the speed of light in the material.

Question 88:

What topology allows multiple devices to be connected to a single communication channel in a network?

Possible Choices:

Point-to-Point Topology

Bus Topology

Star Topology

Multipoint or Multidrop Topology

None of these.

Answer:

Multipoint or multidrop topology allows multiple devices to be connected to a single communication channel, enabling communication between multiple nodes within the network.

Question 89:

What is the main advantage of multipoint or multidrop topology in networking?

Possible Choices:

Simplicity of installation

Reduced network latency

Flexibility in adding or removing devices

Higher network security

None of these.

Answer:

The main advantage of multipoint or multidrop topology is its flexibility, allowing for easy addition or removal of devices without disrupting the network connectivity.

Question 90:

What is the primary function of the buffer jacket in a fiber optic cable?

Possible Choices:

To increase signal attenuation

To enhance light transmission efficiency

To provide mechanical protection to the core and cladding

To facilitate signal amplification

None of these.

Answer:

The buffer jacket of a fiber optic cable is designed to provide mechanical protection to the delicate core and cladding, safeguarding them from damage during installation, handling, and operation.

Question 91:

In multipoint or multidrop topology, what characteristic distinguishes it from other network topologies?

Possible Choices:

Each device has a dedicated communication channel

Devices are connected in a linear sequence

Multiple devices share a single communication channel

Devices are organized in a circular configuration

None of these.

Answer:

In multipoint or multidrop topology, multiple devices share a single communication channel, allowing for communication between multiple nodes within the network. This differs from other topologies where devices may have dedicated communication channels or different interconnection patterns.

Question 92:

What is the primary purpose of Class 2-LP or Class 3-LP cables?

Possible Choices:

Transmitting only power

Transmitting only data

Transmitting both power and data

Transmitting audio signals

None of these.

Answer:

Class 2-LP and Class 3-LP cables are designed to transmit both power and data simultaneously, making them suitable for various applications where devices require power and data connectivity.

Question 93:

Which classification of cables is suitable for low-power applications such as security cameras and access control systems?

Possible Choices:

Class 1-LP

Class 2-LP

Class 3-LP

Class 4-LP

Answer:

Class 2-LP cables are suitable for low-power applications where devices require both power and data transmission, such as security cameras, access control systems, and low-voltage lighting.

Question 94:

Class 3 cables shall have a voltage rating of not less than how many volts?

Possible Choices:

100

154

300

600

1000

Answer:

Class 3 cables shall have a voltage rating of not less than 300 volts. Class 2 and Class 3 cables shall have a temperature rating of not less than 60°C (140°F).

Question 95:

Class 2 and Class 3 cables shall have a temperature rating of no less than how many degree celcius?

Possible Choices:

10

15

30

60

100

Answer:

Class 2 and Class 3 cables shall have a temperature rating of not less than 60°C (140°F).

Question 96:

What type of connectors are commonly used with Class 2-LP or Class 3-LP cables?

Possible Choices:

RJ11

RJ45

USB

BNC

Answer:

RJ45 connectors are commonly used with Class 2-LP or Class 3-LP cables for Ethernet-based applications, providing both power and data connectivity to compatible devices.

Question 97:

What is a key advantage of using Class 2-LP or Class 3-LP cables for power and data transmission?

Possible Choices:

Increased signal attenuation

Reduced installation complexity

Higher power consumption

Limited device compatibility

Answer:

Using Class 2-LP or Class 3-LP cables for power and data transmission reduces installation complexity by eliminating the need for separate power and data cables, resulting in cost savings and simplified deployment of devices.

Question 98:

Cables with the suffix "-LP" shall be permitted to be installed in (chose all that apply):

Possible Choices:

bundles

raceways

cable trays

communications raceways

cable routing assemblies

Answer:

Cables with the suffix "-LP" shall be permitted to be installed in bundles, raceways, cable trays, communications raceways, and cable routing assemblies.

Question 99:

The requirements for obtaining a LVS contractor license in Hawaii include being at least how many years of age?

Possible Choices:

16

18

21

None of these.

Answer:

The requirements for obtaining a LVS contractor license in Hawaii include being at least 18 years of age.

Question 100:

The requirements for obtaining a LVS contractor license in Hawaii include having a minimum of how many years of experience in the low voltage field?

Possible Choices:

1

2

3

4

5

6

None of these.

Answer:

The requirements for obtaining a LVS contractor license in Hawaii include having a minimum of four years of experience in the low voltage field.

Question 101:

Hawaii does not reciprocate with any jurisdiction other than:

Possible Choices:

CA

TX

FL

NY

MI

None of these.

Answer:

None of these. Hawaii does not reciprocate with any jurisdiction.

Question 102:

License is valid for how many years?

<u>Possible Choices:</u>

1

2

3

4

5

None of these.

Answer:

All ELECTRICIAN licenses, regardless of issuance date, are subject to renewal on or before June 30, every three years (triennial renewal) beginning June 1996.

End of Book